The Day the Island Exploded

by

Alexandra Pratt

Illustrated by
Seb Camagajevac

For Graham, whose story this is.
Many thanks.

You do not need to read this page –
just get on with the book!

First published in 2009 in Great Britain by
Barrington Stoke Ltd
18 Walker St, Edinburgh, EH3 7LP

www.barringtonstoke.co.uk

Quotation from the Base Commander's Log used with kind
permission from the British Antarctic Survey

ISBN: 978-1-84299-695-9

Printed in Great Britain by Bell & Bain Ltd

LOTTERY FUNDED

Contents

A Note from the Author

This isn't my story. It's my father-in-law, Graham Seear's story. One day, when we were cleaning out some boxes in his house, I found a pile of dusty old black and white photos. I looked through them, and I couldn't believe what I saw; ice, volcanoes, an island ... what was this? So, Graham sat down and told me all about his big adventure, the day an island in Antarctica exploded.

This story is based on what Graham Seear told me about that day.

In retelling his memories, I have added some details of my own to help the reader picture the action in their mind. But all the events in the story are true.

On the night of the 4th December 1967, the Commander of the British base on Deception Island wrote in his log book:

22:55 GMT: *"Two men prepared to climb ... so that observations could be made from 1150 feet ... ash was falling heavily and had reduced visibility to 30 yards."*

22:58 GMT: *"Started to send radio calls for help ..."*

Introduction
Help!

"Come outside, quick!" shouted Billy, bursting into the room. "I think the island is exploding!"

The other men looked up from their dinner in shock, but Billy had already turned to run back out into the snow. Rushing outside after him into the cold, they all looked at a huge black cloud in the sky. It was close by and loomed over them, raining down ash and hot rocks that smacked into the ground and hissed in the freezing waters of the bay.

"It looks just like an atom bomb!" shouted Graham, the youngest member of the team. But it wasn't a bomb. It was a volcano, and it was erupting for the first time in over 120 years.

The men just stood for a moment, looking in horror, as the cloud became bigger and bigger. Soon it covered almost all of the island and turned the pale evening sky into the blackest night.

What were they to do?

It was 1967 and the 15 men working for the British Survey team in Antarctica were trapped on a piece of rock called Deception Island. They were 2000km from the rest of the world. They had no means of escape and no way of knowing if the world realised what was happening.

Would help arrive in time to save their lives?

Chapter 1
The Dragon's Mouth

A Year Earlier

Graham was just 20 years old when he left the UK on the supply ship called the *Shackleton*, bound for a small island off the coast of the Antarctic. He had taken a job on a British science research base, on Deception Island, because he was young and looking for adventure.

Graham planned to spend the next two years on this island, which would be freezing and snow-covered for much of that time. The island is just 14km across, shaped like a horse-shoe. Inside, there lies a bay defended by huge black cliffs that rise up from the ocean. The British base is no more than a few huts scattered beside the bay. To reach it, ships must pass through a narrow gap in those cliffs, called Neptune's Bellows. This is only possible in summer, when the sea ice retreats.

In the past the island had been used by the British for secret World War II missions. But in 1967 the island was home to just 15 British scientists, led by the Base Commander. Their work involved monitoring weather patterns, surveying the wildlife and providing support and supplies for a number of bases that were even more remote, further south in Antarctica. One of these scientists was Shawn, and he and Graham quickly became close friends.

Graham was not involved in the scientific research. His job, as the station engineer, was to maintain the diesel generators that powered the base and the tractors used for transport in the snow. When he wasn't working, Graham learned to ski and there were other things to do too. The island is home to all kinds of wildlife, including huge leopard seals which hunt the penguin colonies with deadly skill and speed. On sunny days, the men enjoyed climbing the mountain behind the base for the stunning views across the ocean towards the South Pole.

The British base was called Whalers Bay and life there wasn't easy. One of the long, low buildings was wooden and had been built earlier in the 20th century by men from Norway, who came to these cold waters to hunt whales. The second building was more modern and had a kitchen and living spaces, as well as work areas and rooms with bunk-beds for sleeping.

Their only warmth in this wilderness came from a coal fire and a stove in the kitchen that was always kept lit. It was basic, but it was comfy and there was always something to do.

Sometimes, the men left the base to go on short expeditions for research or just for fun. There were risks too. One day, Graham fell through ice into the freezing sea-water below, but he was lucky. His friends pulled him out straight away. A moment longer and the cold would have killed him.

One of the most dangerous things to do was to cross the glacier to the north of the base. A glacier is a large mass of ice formed over thousands of years. Sometimes, the men on the British team risked going across it to visit the small group of scientists who came from Chile in South America and who worked on a base further north along the shore at a place called Pendulum Cove. The two teams would meet up for a meal, or a game of football.

But there was one other very important job the scientists on the island were there to do.

Monitor the volcanoes.

The island has a long history of discovery and adventure. Early explorers thought of passing through the gap to the bay, called Neptune's Bellows, as "going through the mouth of the dragon" because the island is really a ring of volcanoes. When the volcanoes all erupted at the same time in the 19th century, it seemed as though the island was breathing fire.

Graham knew the island was volcanic. When he first arrived there, he found hot springs and bits of burnt cinder crystallised in the ice.

But, Graham thought to himself, *none of the volcanoes have erupted for many, many years. The scientists say the volcanoes are dormant, so we'll be safe.*

He was wrong.

Chapter 2
Warnings

For the first year, Graham was very happy living and working on the base. He soon became used to the routines of work and play. He even became used to the endless cold, and the long dark nights when the temperature fell to -15°C. It was hard to remember there was another world out there, where people watched television and drove cars.

Then the earth-tremors began.

At first the tremors were just small, as though the island was shivering under its coat of ice. But, as the months passed, they became stronger. And stronger.

Strange things had happened before on the island. In 1842, the captain of an American ship that was hunting whales stood on his deck and saw 13 volcanoes erupt, turning the island bright with lava and fire. Then, in 1921, the shore suddenly began to collapse and the sea boiled, stripping paint from the hulls of the ships in the bay.

Were the volcanoes waking up again now?

Other strange things began to happen, too. The penguins should have been starting their breeding season on the rocky shores, but Graham noticed they had all gone.

Yet when the supply ship the *Shackleton* made its once-a-year visit for a few days at the start of the summer, the tremors stopped. The men on the base told the ship's crew about the tremors, but they didn't believe the stories.

"You've been on this island too long!" they joked. "You're going mad!"

Then, something very odd happened. As the ship sailed away a few days later, Graham stood on the shore and noticed that all the small birds who lived on the island were sitting on the ship!

Those little birds could not fly the long distances to the mainland – were they hitching a lift on the ship? And if so, why?

After all the wildlife left, there was a hush, a stillness to the island, that Graham felt was really weird. So weird, he went straight back to his bunk-bed at the base to pack his bags.

"Hey, where are you going? A weekend in Paris?" laughed Shawn, coming into the room. Graham tried to smile.

"You know how animals seem to sense when something bad is going to happen?" said Graham.

"Are you talking about the earthquakes again?" laughed Shawn.

"I just watched the supply ship sail, and all the birds were sitting on the decks! They were all leaving!" said Graham, shoving his kit into a bag.

"What?" Shawn wasn't laughing so much now.

"So if that supply ship comes back, I'm off out of here," said Graham. But they both knew there was little chance of that.

A few days later, something happened to make Graham think that his fears were all too correct. He was alone in one of the sheds, when suddenly, the tractor he was working on just rolled away from him. The earth was moving! Looking up, he saw the big lights in the roof were swinging crazily on their long wires.

A real earthquake!

Graham worried that the shed might collapse on top of him, so he ran outside into the snow. The island itself was shaking!

Then, it just stopped, as though nothing had happened.

Chapter 3
Rumblings

Graham was not the only one to notice what was going on. His friend Shawn and one of the other men did their normal measurements and observations, which included taking the sea temperature in the bay. When they returned to the base one day in early December, Graham saw that they were excited and a little scared.

"What's wrong?" he asked.

"The sea!" said Shawn. "It's four degrees warmer than it was yesterday!"

"*Four degrees!*" Graham almost shouted in surprise. "Is that even possible? If the sea has risen by four degrees since yesterday, what will it be tomorrow?"

The men were silent. No one could answer his questions and they all looked at each other, worried. Then the Commander walked in, shaking snow from his fur-lined hood. He saw the looks on the faces of Graham, Shawn and the other men, who told him about the sea.

But there was nothing their Commander could do.

The supply ship was many miles away by now and the team had no way of escape. They did have a small, light aircraft, but it was only big enough to carry four men at once and it couldn't hold enough fuel to fly to the mainland, anyway.

Later that evening, all the men were sitting down to dinner together. It was often a cheerful time. Graham, Shawn and the other men took it in turns to cook for each other. Some meals were excellent and others best avoided!

It was Shawn's turn to cook and dinner was a success. Then, just as everyone was finishing their dessert, the ground started to shake.

A violent shudder threw the men from their chairs and the building rocked in the snow. Pots and pans flew around the kitchen, crashing into each other and smashing on the floor. It was a second big earthquake, but this time it went on and on. Then, suddenly, it stopped.

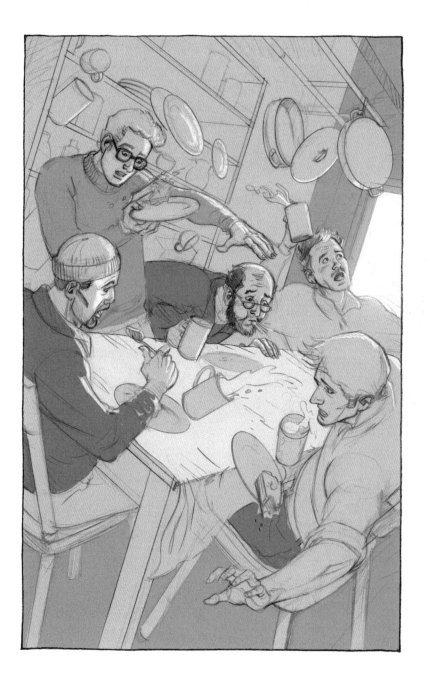

Graham and the others started to laugh with relief.

"There! Just another tremor!" they told each other. "No harm done!"

While the men laughed and chatted in the warm, bright safety of the base, far, far below them, things were happening underground. Big things.

Deep below the ice and great black rocks of the island, beneath even the ocean itself, powerful forces were stirring. Under the island's volcanoes, pressure was building up and up. The heat this created began to melt the glaciers.

Out in the bay, the sea-bed ripped apart, sucking the ocean down into an under-water volcano. Here it hit red-hot lava pushing upwards from deep within the earth.

The earthquake fractured the ground in the north of the island. Huge rocks tumbled and the land opened up, creating a new and deadly volcanic crater.

Yet the men in Whalers Bay and Pendulum Cove knew nothing of this. All they could see was the soft light of an Antarctic summer evening turning the snow-reflecting sky pink and gold.

Everything seemed normal. That was, until Billy ran in with his news and the thing they had all been dreading began.

The island really *was* exploding.

Chapter 4

Nowhere to Run

Graham and the rest of the men looked on in horror as the thick black smoke billowed from the volcano. It was only 3km away to the north and as they stood there, it seemed to the men as if the volcano was almost close enough to touch.

The black cloud grew quickly, and soon all of the island was covered in smog. A sharp taste of burning caught at the back of Graham's throat.

But that wasn't all. Out into the bay, sea-water met the hot lava rising up through an under-water volcano. There was a whoosh and the men turned around in time to see a powerful jet of water and steam shoot high into the sky.

Graham felt helpless as the volcanic vents burst up all around the island. One after another, jets of steam punched through the ice as the super-heated water under the glacier forced its way upwards, spewing out water vapour and smoking rocks.

It seemed as though they had been standing there watching the island erupt for hours, but it was really only a few minutes. Ash was falling so heavily, they could only see a few metres ahead. The white snow turned black. Graham felt like he was in a nightmare. He wanted to run, but his legs wouldn't move. He tried to think, but his mind was filled with confusion and fear.

Would he be boiled to death in the steam? Or choked by the ash?

In his terror, all Graham could remember about volcanoes were school lessons about the ancient city of Pompeii that was destroyed by a mighty volcano. It suffocated every living thing with toxic winds that blew at hundreds of miles an hour. People and animals were encased in a tomb of hot ash.

Here on the island, the red-hot lava was trapped under the ice long enough to cool a little and become solid. So it was thrown up out of the volcano in the form of great pieces of rock. It was lucky for the men that these super-hot rocks were thrown out with so much force that they fell beyond the base and out into the bay, where they made the water boil.

Just when he thought things couldn't get any worse, Graham thought he could just see something else rolling towards them from the skies.

"Gas! It's sulphur!" he shouted in panic. "It's coming across here!"

Seconds later, it hit them. A great cloud of lethal gas that smelt and tasted like rotting eggs. The wind was blowing this gas from the volcano directly towards the British base. Graham's eyes began to water and the gas made him choke and gasp for breath.

"Get inside!" shouted the Commander, coughing. "Everyone inside! Now!"

In fear for their lives, the men dashed for the safety inside. Yet the wooden huts were already half engulfed by the ash. It wouldn't be long before the ash covered the buildings, blocking the windows and doors. How safe would the base really be?

Were they going to be buried alive?

Just then, Shawn asked, "What about the team at Pendulum Cove? It looked as though that main eruption was almost on top of their base. Do you think they're still alive?"

The Commander was already using the radio.

"Pendulum Cove, come in … Pendulum Cove. What is your status? Over."

The crackling sound of static filled the room. The Commander tried again.

"Pendulum Cove, this is the British team at Whalers Bay, come in. Over."

This time, there wasn't even static, just silence. Graham and Shawn looked at each other and then looked at the Commander, but he didn't need to say anything. All the men knew the truth.

The island was erupting. They were totally alone and there was nowhere to run. It was going to be the longest night of their lives.

Chapter 5
Calling for Help

However bad things were at the British base, the Commander knew that they must be much worse for the other team.

"Now, it looks like that volcano is right on top of those guys," he said.

All the men nodded.

"We've got those two small boats with outboard motors. Graham, Shawn, I want you to take them up the bay to Pendulum

Cove and see what you can do. Maybe some of the men are still alive, and we can rescue them."

There was a short silence. Everyone in the room knew that this rescue mission could mean death for Graham and Shawn. Motor across a bay sprayed with super-hot rocks *towards* the main volcano?

"OK," said Graham. It was highly risky, he knew, but someone needed to go out there and help the other team. Graham pushed the fear out of his mind and took a deep breath. He lifted his chin and looked at Shawn with one eyebrow raised. Shawn gave him a steady look and nodded.

Graham and Shawn tied scarves around their heads to avoid breathing in the ash. They forced open the hut door against the weight of fallen ash and rocks. Outside, the sky was dark. The land that was once white was now black and there was still a foul smell in the air.

"Sulphur!" gasped Graham and Shawn nodded. Speaking was pointless against the high winds and choking clouds.

Pointing towards the boats, Graham led the way towards the jetty. As they staggered closer, they noticed something very odd about the water in the bay.

It had gone.

Normally, the two little boats would be tied up to the jetty, ready to be used by the men for moving around the bay, but now the water was gone and the boats sat on dry ground. As the two men stared in shock at the place where the sea used to be, Graham noticed movement, out in the gloom of the bay.

"Watch out!" he cried, pushing Shawn further up the shore. "It's a tidal wave. A tsunami!"

They rushed for the safety of higher ground. Panic and the effort of running up-hill through the ash made them breathe heavily, until the dry air tore painfully at their throats. For those few seconds, all Graham could think about was the huge wave sweeping towards them out of the darkness. The moment they reached safety, the wave crashed on the shore below, smashing the jetty and the boats.

Then, just as suddenly, the same water seemed to be sucked away, leaving what was left of the boats high and dry again. Seconds later, another big wave surged towards the land, this time almost soaking Graham, and Shawn, who were standing high above the shore.

"Let's get out of here!" yelled Shawn, and he didn't need to say it twice!

Feeling shaken, Graham and Shawn struggled as quickly as they could back into the huts. The ash was now knee-deep on the ground.

"We're not going anywhere in those boats, sir," said Shawn. "They're on the ground." And he explained what they had seen.

"Right." Grim faced, the Commander took the radio from the man trying to contact the other team, and opened the frequency in the hope that someone – anyone – might hear them.

"May-day. May-day," he said. "This is British Antarctic Base on Deception Island. May-day. May-day."

Chapter 6
The Longest Night

"There's no reply." The Commander looked up from the radio. "What's happening out there?"

"I'll look, sir," said Shawn. A few moments later, he fell back in through the door, blackened from head to foot. "It's not just ash now, sir, there's everything from big rocks to sand. And there's something else. I think those clouds are going to cause a storm."

At that moment a brilliant flash lit the room for a second and was followed by a crash of thunder so loud that the tea-cups rattled on the tables.

"It's an electrical storm!" shouted Graham.

Another bolt of lightning lit up the room and some men put their hands over their ears, ready for the thunder.

"The storm is jamming the radio, sir," said the radio operator, who was sending message after message with no reply.

The Commander nodded.

"Keep sending those distress signals anyway. Someone must hear us. In the meantime, prepare to evacuate. When our chance comes to get off the island, we must be ready to take it."

While the other men rushed to pack as Graham had several days before. He sat and looked through the last small window not covered by ash and sand. There was an eerie silence between rolls of thunder. The sky was black and so was their future. At any moment, he thought, they could be killed by red-hot lava, swept away by a tidal wave, or buried alive under the ash.

A few months earlier, it had been Graham's 21st birthday. Now he wondered, with a cold shiver, if it would be his last. In this brief moment of stillness, Graham allowed himself to think about all the things he might never see or do again; his home in England, his parents, even the children he might never have.

This job was turning out to be a bit more of an adventure than he had expected!

Graham put such thoughts out of his mind and tried to focus on how they could escape. But was there anyone out there to rescue them, anyway? Graham could not think of another British ship in the area and although there were British bases on other islands, they had no way of reaching them.

Just then, a crackling voice broke into his thoughts.

"Deception Island ... Deception Island. We read you. What is your status? Over."

"Sir!" shouted Graham, jumping up. "Sir! Someone heard us!"

The Commander rushed back into the radio room as the voice said, "This is the British Base on Argentine Island. Say again. Over."

"This is Deception Island," said the Commander, slowly and clearly into the radio receiver. "Island has erupted. Request permission to evacuate. Over."

"Message received ..." The sound of static again rang out.

"It's gone again, sir," said the operator, twisting the radio dials to no effect.

Just then, a very loud drumming noise drowned out the sound of static.

"What the ...?" said Graham.

Shawn opened the door and tried to shut it again straight away, but struggled, as though a great weight was pressing on it from the other side. Graham ran over to help him.

"It's ice, sir." Shawn gasped as they finally clicked the door into place. "Like hail-stones, only they're the size of golf balls."

Would they crush the base?

Chapter 7
Across the Glacier

Hours ticked by in the darkness. Some men prayed, others tried to keep their spirits up by chatting and joking.

Sometime in the early hours of the morning, a crackling message came through on the radio from the British base on Argentine Island that their British supply ship, the *Shackleton*, had been contacted. Her estimated time of arrival was 3pm the following afternoon. All knew this would almost certainly be too late.

Before they could talk further, another crash of the electric storms overhead again cut the connection.

Graham couldn't believe it when, an hour or so later, the sound of knocking was heard between crashes of thunder. All the men looked at each other in surprise. None of them was outside and the other team was on the other side of the glacier, in the shadow of the volcano itself. Surely they weren't still alive?

The knocking became a hammering and the Commander tugged open the door. Ash and ice fell into the room, but in the doorway were several men and all were barely able to stand.

"*Buenos noches*. Good evening," said one in Spanish with a small smile. The man was the Chief at the other base, and was known by most of the British team.

"Come in! Welcome!" The British made space for the handful of men who staggered through the door and into the now very cramped hut.

"Is this all of you?" the British Commander asked the Chief in a low voice, thinking of the 27 men he knew were based at Pendulum Cove. There were no more than 15 here.

"For now, yes," replied the Chief, "but the others will join us soon – I hope."

Just then, another two men almost fell through the doorway into the welcoming warmth of the base. Graham, Shawn and all the other British team were busy, making food and hot drinks for their guests, as well as offering their spare kit, as the other

team's clothes were blackened, ripped and stinking.

"Tell us what happened!" said Billy, hopeful that they all might yet live through this disaster. If these men could walk out from under the volcano, surely there was some hope for them all?

"The explosion – the eruption ..." began the Chief slowly, "it is very, very close to our base." He paused again, as though it was painful to remember.

Then he went on, "Each time the volcano exploded, large rocks fell all around us. Some were three, four metres across – the size of a truck!"

Graham and Shawn looked at each other. Maybe they had been lucky, after all!

"The sea-water began to boil," said the Chief. "We thought it was because so many burning rocks fell in the water, but it was really because there is a second big volcano out in the bay!"

This was bad news indeed and the British team looked at each other grimly.

The Chief took a sip of his tea and continued. "We hid in the basement, it has no windows. But when the storms began, there were such huge explosions, such wild winds and the sulphur was so strong, we knew we were in immediate danger. Our only hope was to walk south, here to your base."

At that moment, another small group of men arrived and were given something to eat. Now, 21 had made the journey. What about the 6 others?

The Chief continued, "It is 3km across the glacier and the ground is black with ash and slippery with melted ice. We all left safely, but we got split up, because the underground tremors threw us off the path ... but the greatest dangers were the crevasses."

The British team nodded. They knew that a crevasse, a gap in the glacier, could be a few centimetres or a few metres across, but they were always very deep and if a man fell into one, it was almost impossible to escape.

"Yes," the Chief went on. "A deep layer of ash now covers the ice and it was impossible to see where it was safe to tread. The only light came from the red glow of the volcanic craters themselves. All the time, we feared a land-slide or that a river of boiling lava would come out of the darkness."

"When did you start walking?" asked Graham

"Oh, hours ago ..." the Chief stopped as the 6 last men of his team entered the base. They all hugged each other with relief.

"I can't believe they all made it," said Shawn in a low voice to Graham, who nodded. It seemed like a miracle, but were they really any safer here than at Pendulum Cove?

Chapter 8
Contact

As the men from the other base rested, the storm subsided and the radio once again crackled. Everyone sat up and listened carefully as a distant voice struggled to make itself heard.

"I don't think it is the British base on Argentine Island, sir," said the radio operator. Then, the voice became stronger and all heard it clearly.

"This is the ship *Pilato Pardo*, come in." The men from the other team let out a small cheer. "What is your status? Over."

"It's your supply ship!" said the Commander looking at the Chief and taking the receiver.

"We copy, *Pilato Pardo*, this is the British base on Deception Island. Report no casualties. All your personnel are safe here at Whalers Bay. Over."

"Our estimated time of arrival is 0400 hours," replied the voice from the ship. "What are conditions in the bay? Over."

At that moment, the sound of static cut the signal, but it didn't damp the spirits of the men in that room. There were going to be saved!

"Graham and Shawn," said the Commander, turning to the two friends. "The supply ship is going to need to know what conditions are like out there. Will you go and see? I need wind speed, visibility and I also need to know if the water levels in the bay are still rising and falling as before."

It wasn't a welcome task, but Graham and Shawn happily put their outdoor kit on once again to brave the storm. Anything if it meant rescue!

As they stumbled through the darkness toward the shore, it seemed conditions had improved a little. There were no rivers of red-hot lava flowing towards them, the ice storm had stopped and even the ash fall was reduced.

The water in the bay though, was rising and falling as violently as ever. Each time it rushed forward, the men could see a powerful current sweeping through the narrow gap.

No ship could come through there and not be wrecked. What could the captain do?

Back at the base, the radio was once again crackling and Shawn explained what they had seen to the Commander as the radio operator made contact with the ship's captain.

Communication was difficult through the static and despite the message, the reply came again, "Can a small boat come through the gap into the bay? Over."

They're thinking of sending the life-boats! Graham and Shawn looked at each other. Were they crazy? If the ship couldn't make it, no small life-boat could!

"Negative," replied the Commander. "Repeat, negative ..."

The long night dragged by. Graham had never seen such utter darkness. There was no light from the moon or a single star. The island was wrapped in thick black smoke from the eruptions.

Three hours later, at 0700 hours, no sun could be seen in the east, only a faint grey lightened some of the deeper shadows. Another message crackled over the airwaves.

"We're sailing into the bay ..." followed by the sound of static. Was this their rescue?

"They'll be killed!" said Shawn

"And we'll never escape," replied Graham, looking up at the sky for light and the hope that always comes with it.

The British Commander sat by the radio and sent message after message into the static. He described the conditions and advised against the use of boats, hoping the supply ship would hear them and not risk coming through the gap into the bay. Then, finally, at 10:30 in the morning, the sky turned a pale grey, the smoke cleared and a message came clearly –

"We're sending helicopters in one hour."

Chapter 9
Race Against Time

Unlike the British supply ship, the *Pilato Pardo* always carried two very small helicopters on board. As the first helicopter emerged out of the grey mist of water vapour and ash, Graham realised with a shock it could carry only two men at a time and there were 42 men on the base.

At any moment, any one of those smoking volcanic craters could eject fire high into the sky, killing them all. Would the pilots have enough time to rescue everyone?

The other team was airlifted off first to their supply ship and Graham watched their faces as they went. He saw tiredness, fear, joy and thankfulness. The pilots were flying in poor visibility, out of radio contact, with great danger to their rotor blades from all the falling rock and ash. But there was no choice. They were heroes.

When Graham's turn came, he climbed into the helicopter with a sense of total relief. But there was also a little bit of regret that his journey of a lifetime should end like this. As the helicopter spiralled away into the sky, Graham saw below him the place where his life had almost ended. The island was ravaged – a smoking mess of mud, ash, dark volcanic rocks and even the shimmering blue waters of the bay were now no more than a dirty yellow soup.

Later that afternoon, Graham and his team-mates transferred to the British supply ship, the *Shackleton*. The men from the other team sailed away in the *Pilato Pardo* to the safety of South America. Two days later, the Captain of the British ship decided the volcanoes were quiet enough to allow the ship to sail back into the bay for the team to collect their kit and any valuable equipment left behind.

The afternoon of December 7th was clear and sunny, but as Graham stood on the deck, he felt uneasy as he saw menacing smoke plumes drift from the mountain peaks of the island.

It was a risk, of course, but thrilling, too. What would they find on the island they had so recently escaped?

As the ship sailed slowly through the gap into the bay, all the men gasped. There was a new island in the centre of the bay!

"That's the second volcano!" said Shawn. "I can see the crater!"

The ship dropped its anchor and the men were feeling nervous as they motored to shore in a small boat. Graham ran into the buildings and picked up his bags, still neatly packed from earlier in the week. It all seemed so long ago now!

The other men collected aircraft spares and important papers, then quickly threw a few belongings into bags and fled the huts, which were almost totally buried in ash and ice.

Suddenly, there was a deep rumbling in the air around them. It came up through the soles of Graham's feet and filled his head. Gases fizzed around the rim of the biggest crater, while more black ash and smoke began to boil upwards into the sky. Had it been a terrible mistake to return?

"Come on, let's go!" shouted Graham. As the men ran for the boat, the eruption became stronger.

"It's going in cycles!" panted Shawn as they scrambled up the rope ladder onto deck. "It's going to go off again!"

Sure enough, as the British supply ship steamed out of the bay (more quickly than she had arrived) more smoke and ash poured into the sky.

The men shouted out in fear.

Several new volcanoes exploded right across the island. One after the other, a line of smoking black vents filled the clear blue sky. The glacier tore apart in a great rift and huge rocks crashed down as the ground

heaved. A giant mud-slide smashed through the wall of the crater above the base at Pendulum Cove and swept through the buildings, destroying them.

They had left just in time!

As they sailed safely away, Graham turned and looked at the island for the last time. The volcanoes made a ring of smoking craters around the island, just as the American Captain had seen over a hundred years before in 1842.

They had finally escaped from the mouth of the dragon.

What Happened Later?

Graham went on to work all over the world as a ship's engineer, but he never went back to Antarctica or the island.

The Team

Nine of the men on the British base returned home after the eruption, the rest were sent to other British bases in the Antarctic.

What Happened a Year Later?

A year later, in 1968, five men were sent to the island. Late one night, they were suddenly hurled from their beds by a massive earthquake. One man later swore that when he put his ear to the ground, he could hear the quakes approaching from far off. They were followed by a terrifying electric storm and heavy falls of ash. This time, the buildings and the jetty of the British base were swept away by a river of mud, rocks and melted glacier water.

The men survived, but they faced the volcano without shelter or equipment. One man was hit on the head by a block of ice. They spent the rest of that night outside with nothing more than metal sheets of corrugated iron held above their heads to protect them from the deadly rain of ice and super-hot rocks.

Just as in 1967, these men were also picked up the next morning by a helicopter from the supply ship, the *Pilato Pardo*.

The Island

The volcanic eruptions of 1968-1969 scarred the island with a deep gash from sea to sea. It was over 150m wide, and the men who looked over the edge saw, far beyond the ice of the broken glacier and the swirls of smoke and toxic gases, the bubbling lava deep inside the earth.

Today, that fire still burns beneath the snow and ice of Deception Island.

Barrington Stoke would like to thank all its readers for commenting on the manuscript before publication and in particular:

Tillie Adby
Belqeis Hosan Alfaity
Alham Alqahtani
Courtney Baudry
Sara Binsang
Lucy Bishop
Jasmin Blakeley
Kynsie Brown
Jemma Cooper
Megan Corr
Megan Cowles
Lauren Crockett
Stephen Dilks
Ellise Fowler
Joel Fowler
Zoe-Ann Gardiner
Charlotte Gegg
Johnny Giles
Adrian Hanshaw
Alison Hills
Sophie Kirtly

Matthew Knowles
Nicola Kober
Bianca Lee
Jo Matheson
Bethany McConnell
Fian Moore
Hanna Muldoon
Sundas Munir
Simran Kaur Notay
Sarah Pill
Tomdem Ralson
Conner Robinson
Sinead Ruddock
Lizzie Sarchet
Phinnola Slater
Semhar Solomon
Pip Throughton
Georgia Townsend
Rebecca Triggs
Emma West

Become a Consultant!

Would you like to give us feedback on our titles before they are published? Contact us at the email address below – we'd love to hear from you!

info@barringtonstoke.co.uk
www.barringtonstoke.co.uk

Graham's Album: Deception Island

Want to find out more about Graham's real-life adventure on Deception Island?

Check out his photo album!

To watch a film and to find out even more about Graham's trip to Deception Island, check out www.barringtonstoke.co.uk

These small huts had been used by people who hunted whales a hundred years ago. When I lived there, the huts were heated by open fires and a stove in the kitchen, even when it was 15 degrees below zero outside!

I was feeling nervous when our ship, the Shackleton, left after my first year on the island. Would I see home again?

The ship looked tiny as it sailed away through Neptune's Bellows.

Mount Pond is the highest point on Deception Island and we would often climb up it for the amazing views across the ocean to the Antarctic mainland.

Leopard seals are well named, because they are deadly. They are so big, they can easily kill a man. Look at those teeth!

This is me falling through the ice. A few more minutes in the water and I would have died!

We were lucky that all the huskie dogs we kept on the island left on the ship before the volcanoes started to erupt.

Once we were on board our rescue ship, the island erupted again ...

You don't ever want to get this
close to a volcano!